The World
at
your Feet

For Ben and Jack – my own memory makers,
and anyone who ever wondered or worried. It's OK, you know... you got this. – K.N.

For Lucy, the one always telling me, 'You've got this!'
Thank you for your support and encouragement every day. – C.A.

A STUDIO PRESS BOOK

First published in the UK in 2022 by Studio Press Books,
an imprint of Bonnier Books UK,
4th Floor, Victoria House, Bloomsbury Square, London WC1B 4DA
Owned by Bonnier Books,
Sveavägen 56, Stockholm, Sweden

www.bonnierbooks.co.uk

Text © Karl Newson 2022
Illustrations © Clara Anganuzzi 2022

1 3 5 7 9 10 8 6 4 2

FSC
www.fsc.org
MIX
Paper from
responsible sources
FSC® C104723

Edited by Emma Drage and Ellie Rose
Designed by Nia Williams and Rob Ward
Production Emma Kidd

A CIP catalogue for this book is available from the British Library
Printed and bound in China

The World at your Feet

Karl Newson

illustrated by

Clara Anganuzzi

STUDIO
PRESS

Who?
What?
Where?

Why?

I don't really know
but I'll give it a try.

It's OK, you know, to just not know.
Sometimes I haven't a clue!

All you can be is your best, when you can.

Be up.

Be down.

But be you.

It's OK to wonder and ask yourself "Why?"
And it's OK to just say "Goodbye."

Sometimes goodbye is another hello ...
It's OK to give it a try.

It's OK if something just doesn't work out.
Some days and sometimes they just don't.
And not because you didn't give it your best ...

Some days and sometimes they just won't.

There are things
that we have.

There are things
that we've had.

There are things that are here
though they're not.

Our memories come out of many a
thing we think we once forgot.

Memories come
        and memories go.

And some become
        stories to share.

Sometimes a memory comes back along
to remind us we were there.

There you were
and here you are!
As old as you are today ...

With a head that can think
and a heart that can love
and a mouth full of things to say!

There's a world at your feet and a sun in the sky,
with the birds and the moon and the stars.

It's a place you can roam and a place to call home.

It's yours and it's mine ...

... it's OURS!

We're all here together, alone or apart.
And we all have a story to tell.

And it's OK, you know,
if it makes you feel small …

Often I feel small as well.

But it's not about whether you're BIG or you're small.

If you're STRONG

or how *fast* you can run.

It's more about all of the things you could do,
than the things you have already done.

Wherever you are in this big world of ours,
it's with you that your stories begin.

You could do **anything!**

You could go anywhere!

Just remember, you can't always win.

Be your best when you can.
If you can't, that's OK.

Everybody falls once in a while.

But there's only one you who can do what you do ...

Sing it loud with your heart and your smile!

It's OK, you know,
to just not know
how each story ends.

Yes, there's only one you but you're far from alone when your stories are shared with friends.